Seven Easy-to-Read Stories

Seven Easy-to-Read Stories

by **Grace Maccarone**

Scholastic Reader — Level 1

SCHOLASTIC INC.

Cartwheel B·O·O·K·S ®

New York   Toronto   London   Auckland   Sydney
Mexico City   New Delhi   Hong Kong   Buenos Aires

The Sleep Over
To Lia
— G.M.

To Isaac, Wes, Leo, and Arlo
— B.L.

I Have a Cold
To Mom, who is always ready with the soup, toast, and tea
— G.M.

To Edie Weinberg
— B.L.

I Shop with My Daddy
To Jordan and Steve, my favorite shoppers
— G.M.

For my dad
— D.B.

I See a Leaf
To Jill
— G.M.

For Mom
— L.F.

Softball Practice
For James, Jordan, Julia, and Will
— G.M.

For Grace Maccarone and Edie Weinberg, my two great teammates
— B.L.

Itchy, Itchy Chicken Pox
To Jordan
— G.M.

*To Taylor Duffy and Austin Geary, in hopes that this book
will comfort them if and when they see their first spots*
— B.L.

The 100th Day
To Megan
— G.M.

*To the beginning readers and writers
at Laurel Plains Elementary School*
— A.P.

For Jimmy
— L.F.

30 L

210 L

8R

70 L

8R

80 L

3R

THE SLEEP OVER

by **Grace Maccarone**

Illustrated by **Betsy Lewin**

Sam packs PJ's,
underwear.
Sam does not
pack Huggy Bear.

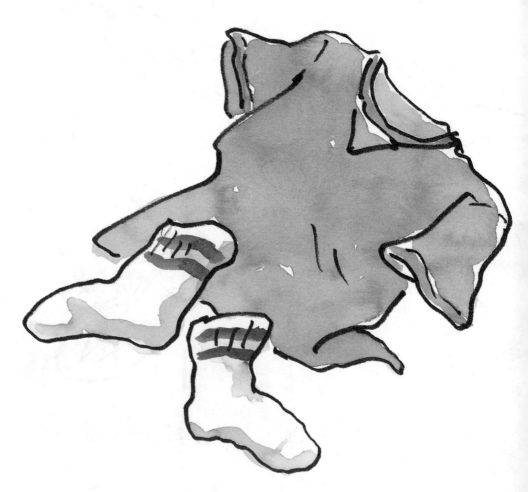

Sam packs a comb,
fresh clothes to wear,
a toothbrush . . .

and his Huggy Bear.

Sam gets inside
the SUV.

"Tonight I'll sleep at
Dan's. Yippee!"

"Come here," says Mom.
"Let me kiss you.
Have fun tonight.
I will miss you!"

"Come in," Dan says.
"I'm glad you came.
Max is here.
Let's play a game."

They play a game,
then play another.

"It's time to eat, boys," calls Dan's mother.

Sam is hungry,
so Sam eats a
salad and a slice
of pizza.

They brush their teeth

and wash their faces,

put on pajamas...

and pick their places.

"Let's watch a movie on TV,"
Dan says.
The other boys agree.

At ten o'clock,
the movie ends.
It's sleepy time
for three good friends.

Dan's mom comes in
to close the light.
She says, "Good night.
Sweet dreams. Sleep tight."

But Sam needs
Huggy.

He goes to get her.

Now Sam has Huggy,
and Sam feels better.

But Sam can't sleep.
He misses his mother.
He misses his dad.
He misses his brother.

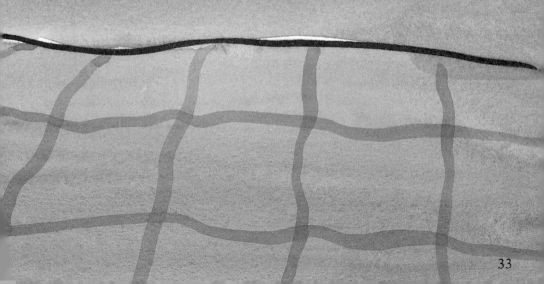

He tells Dan's mom.

She tells Sam's dad.

Now Dad is here,
and Sam is glad.

So Sam goes home.

He gets there fast.

And Sam is in
his bed —
at last!

When morning comes,
Sam's on his way
to Dan's where he'll
eat eggs and play.

The three boys
have a happy day!

I Have a Cold

by **Grace Maccarone**

Illustrated by **Betsy Lewin**

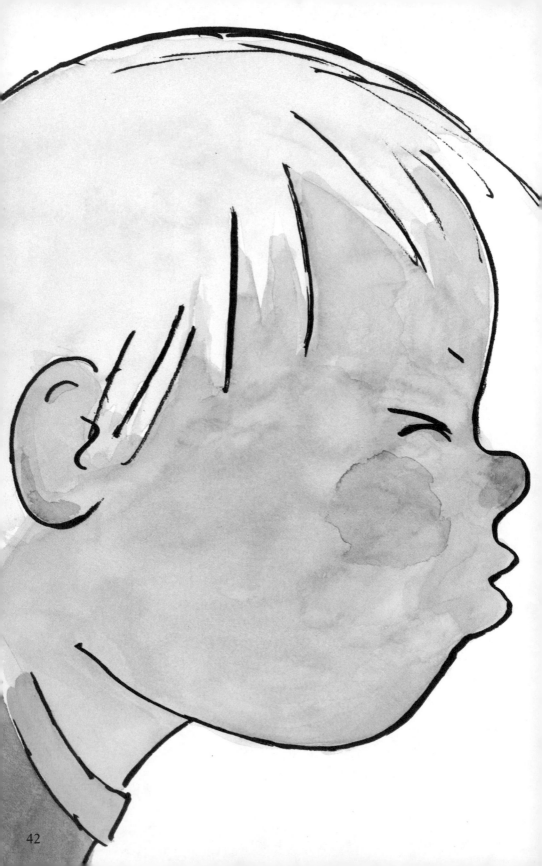

Ah-choo!

Ah-choo!

I sneeze and sneeze.

May I have
a tissue, please?

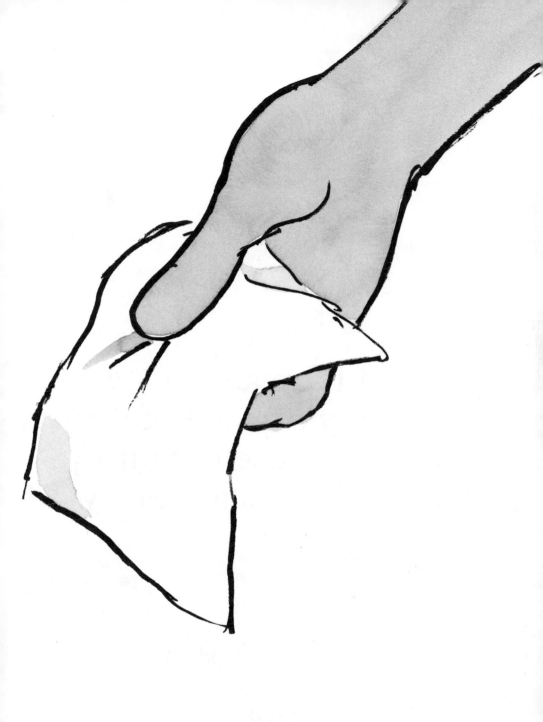

I have a cold.
My ears are stuffy.
My nose is runny.
My eyes are puffy.

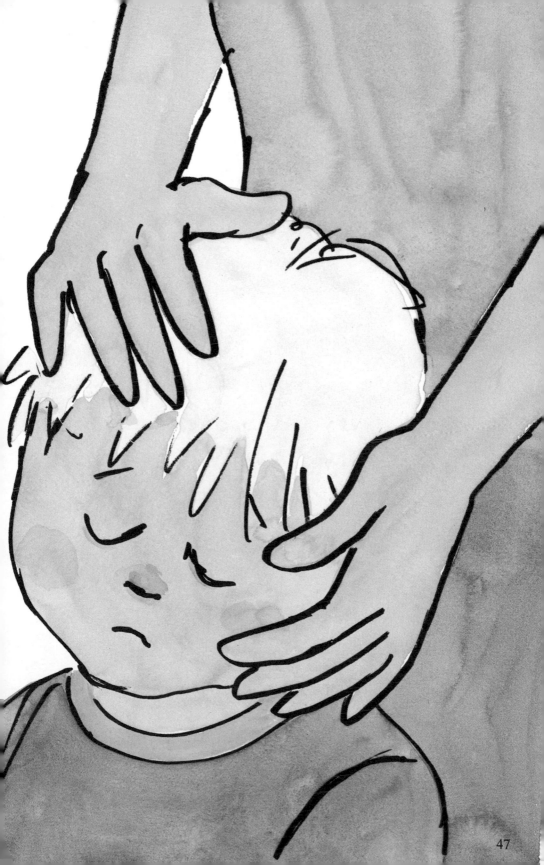

Ah-choo!
    Ah-choo!
I sneeze and sneeze.

I blow my nose.
Excuse me, please.

I read a book.

51

I watch TV.

Mom brings me soup
and toast and tea.

Ah-choo! Ah-choo!
I sneeze and sneeze.

I'm getting sick of this disease!

My nose is stuffy.
My eyes are red.
I sniffle. I snuffle.
I go to bed.

I make mountains
with my knees.

Dolphins, sharks,
and manatees
swim around
in blanket seas.

Dad gives me
something in a spoon.
He says that
I'll feel better soon.

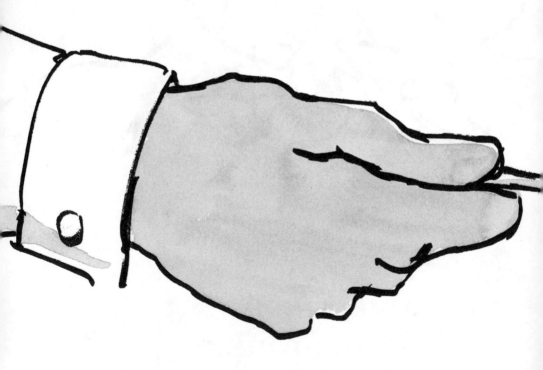

I hold my nose,
and down it goes.

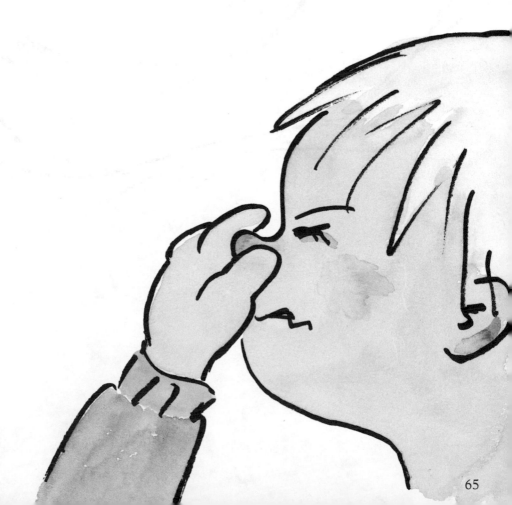

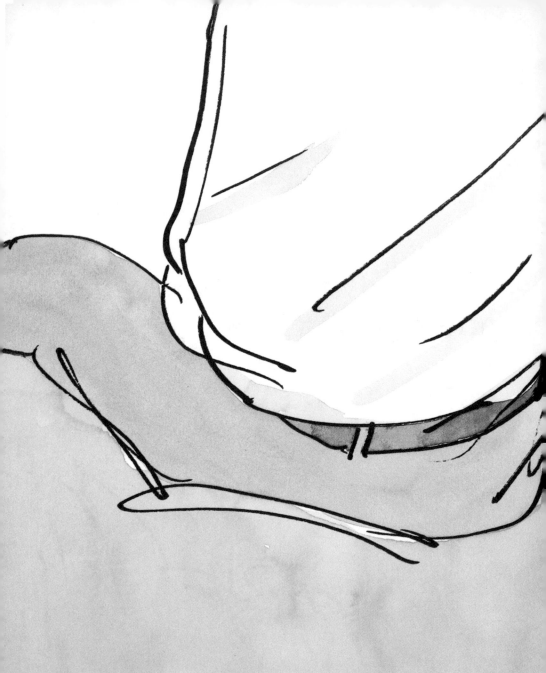

Dad tucks me in,
and then I doze.

Before I fall asleep,
I pray
that my bad cold
will go away.

Tomorrow, I'll go out and play!

I Shop with My Daddy

by **Grace Maccarone**

Illustrated by **Denise Brunkus**

We drive to the store.

I open the door.

We take a cart

and now we start.

We take carrots.

We take cherries.

We take apples.

We take berries.

I take milk

My dad takes cheese.

"Can we get
some cookies, please?"

Daddy says, "Not today."
So I put them away.

We take chicken.

We take meat.

We take fish.

I want a treat.

Daddy says, "Not today."

So I put it away.

I take corn.

My dad takes peas.

"Can we get
some candy, please?"

Daddy says, "Not today."
So I put it away.

We take beans and rice
and spaghetti.

We take bread,
and we are ready.

It is time
for us to pay.

We pack our bags.

"Good-bye," we say.

One more thing—

and we're on our way.

I See a Leaf

Story by **Grace Maccarone**
Illustrated by **Laura Freeman**

Kate and Jill are walking to school.

"I see a leaf," says Jill.

"I will give it to Miss Hill."

"I see a leaf," says Kate.

"I will give it to Miss Hill."

Kate and Jill see Jack.
"I have a red leaf
for Miss Hill," says Kate.
"Jill has a yellow leaf
for Miss Hill."

"So?" says Jack.
"I will give her
two leaves…

four leaves…

more and more leaves!"

Jill, Kate, and Jack
carry the leaves to class.
They see Miss Hill.

"This red leaf is for you,"
says Kate.
"This yellow leaf is for you,"
says Jill.

"These are for you,"
says Jack.
Miss Hill is surprised.

"Thank you,"
says Miss Hill.
"Let's make a tree."

And they do.

SOFTBALL PRACTICE

by **Grace Maccarone**
Illustrated by **Betsy Lewin**

Softball practice
is at four.
Sam gets his stuff,
runs out the door.

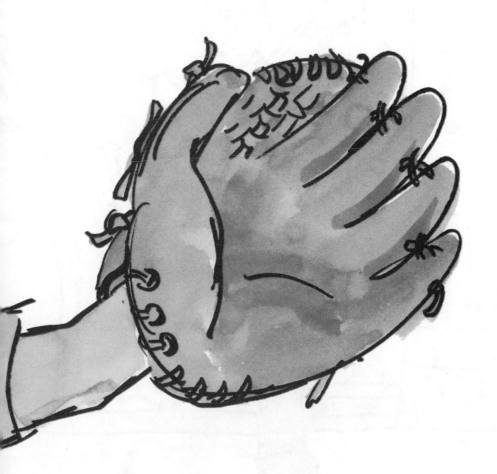

He goes inside
a yellow van

and says hello
to his friend Jan.

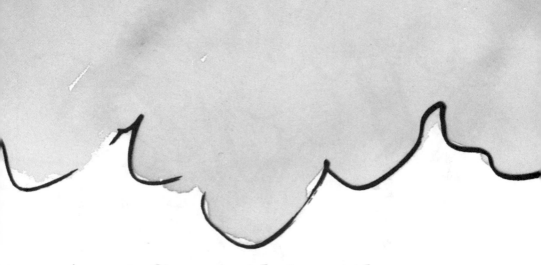

Aunt Gracie drives them
to a park...

but doesn't stay.
She drives away.

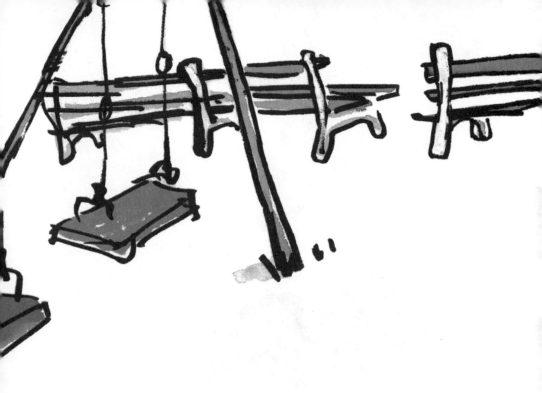

"We're first," says Sam.
"We have to wait."
And so they wait...

and wait . . .

and wait.

And then Sam says,
"It's getting late.
We are waiting too long.
Something is wrong."

A worried look
is on Jan's face.
She says, "My Aunt Grace
left us at the wrong place."

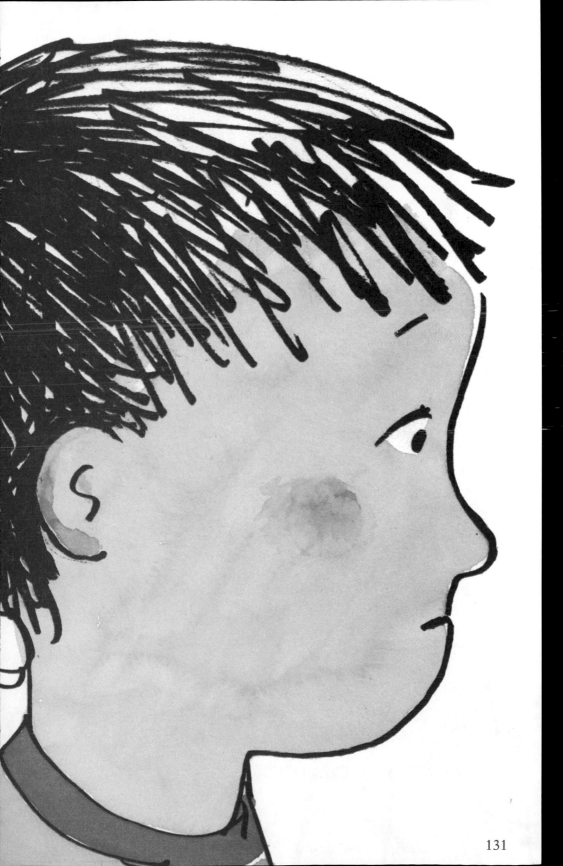

Sam says,
"Don't worry, Jan."
Sam says,
"I have a plan.

"You throw to me.
Then I'll throw to you.
We will practice together."
And that's what they do.

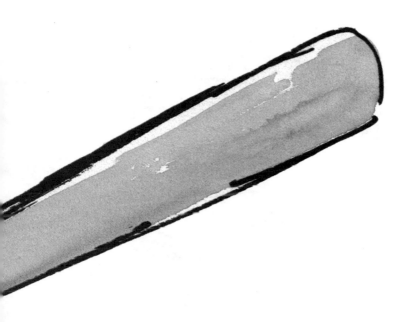

Jan is up. Sam pitches.

Jan swings.

And they run.
They practice together.
They have lots of fun.

Now here comes Sam's mom.

And here comes Jan's dad.

And here comes Aunt Gracie,
feeling quite bad.

There are hugs for all.

Then everyone plays ball!

Itchy, Itchy Chicken Pox

by **Grace Maccarone**

Illustrated by **Betsy Lewin**

A spot.
A spot.
Another spot.

Uh-oh!
Chicken pox!

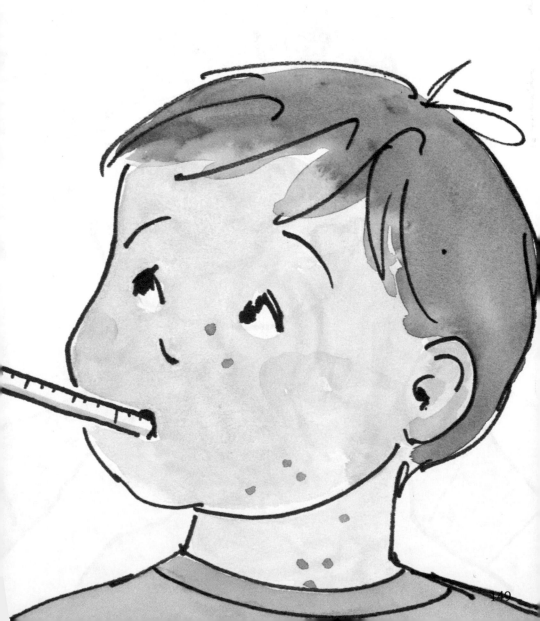

Under my shirt.
Under my socks.

Itchy, itchy
chicken pox.

Don't rub.
Don't scratch.

Oh, no!
Another batch!

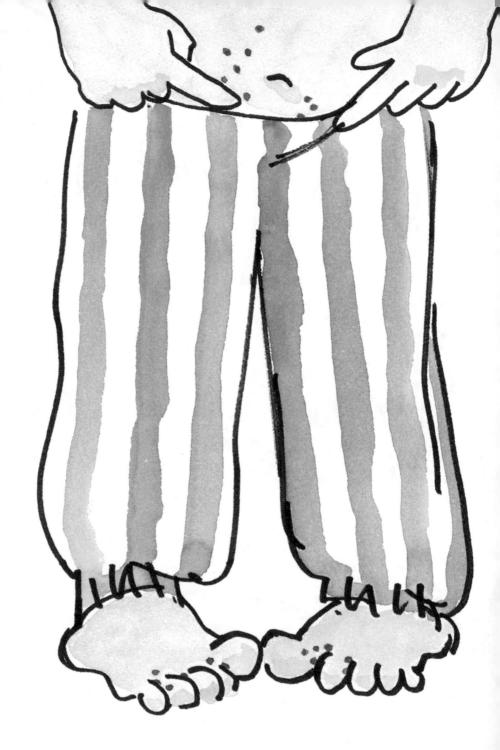

On my tummy,
between my toes,

down my back,
on my nose!

Lotion on.
Itching's gone
just for now.

It comes back—
OW!

One and two
and three and four.
Five and six…
and more and more.

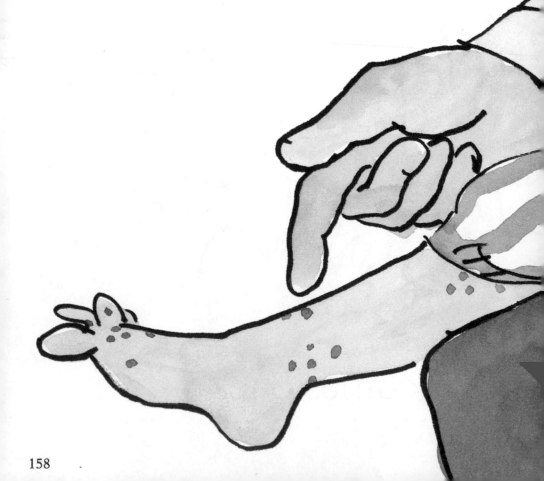

159

Daddy counts
my itchy spots.
Lots and lots
of chicken pox.

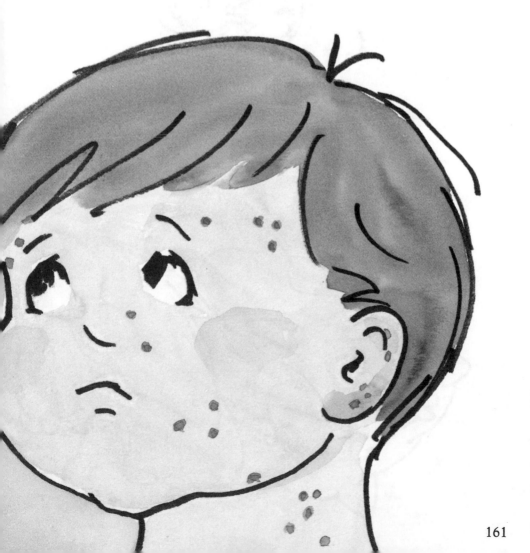

Itchy, itchy,
I feel twitchy....

I run away.
The itching stays.

Rubber ducky doesn't
like my yucky, mucky
oatmeal bath.
But Mommy says
it's good for me.

I rest.

I read.

I eat.

I play.

I feel better
every day.

And then...
no new spots.
Hooray!

I'm okay!
I get to go
to school today!

The 100th Day

Story by **Grace Maccarone**

Literacy Activities by **Alayne Pick**

Illustrated by **Laura Freeman**

Today is the 100th day of school in Miss Hill's class.

Jill likes to make things.
She uses 100 beads
to make four necklaces.
Each necklace has 25 beads.

Jack does not want
to make necklaces.

Ben likes to write stories.

He writes about 100 cats.

20 are black.

20 are orange.

20 are white.

20 are gray.

20 have stripes.

Jack does not want
to write a story.

Kate likes to draw.

She draws 100 stars.
50 are silver.
50 are gold.

Jack does not want
to draw.
What will Jack do?

Jack looks out the window.

He wants to run.

He wants to jump.

Jack has an idea.

He will jump to 100.

Can he do it?

Jill gets the rope.
She and Ben turn it.
Everyone counts together
as Jack jumps.

1 2 3 4 5 6
7 8 9 10 11 12 13
14 15 16 17 18 19 20
21 22 23 24 25
26 27 28 29
30 31 32 33 34
35 36 37 38 39
40 41 42 43 44 45
46 47 48 49 50

51 52 53 54 55 56
57 58 59 60 61 62
63 64 65 66 67
68 69 70 71 72
73 74 75 76 77 78
79 80 81 82 83
84 85 86 87 88
89 90 91 92
93 94
95 96 97 98 99

100!
Hooray for Jack!

Happy Handwriting

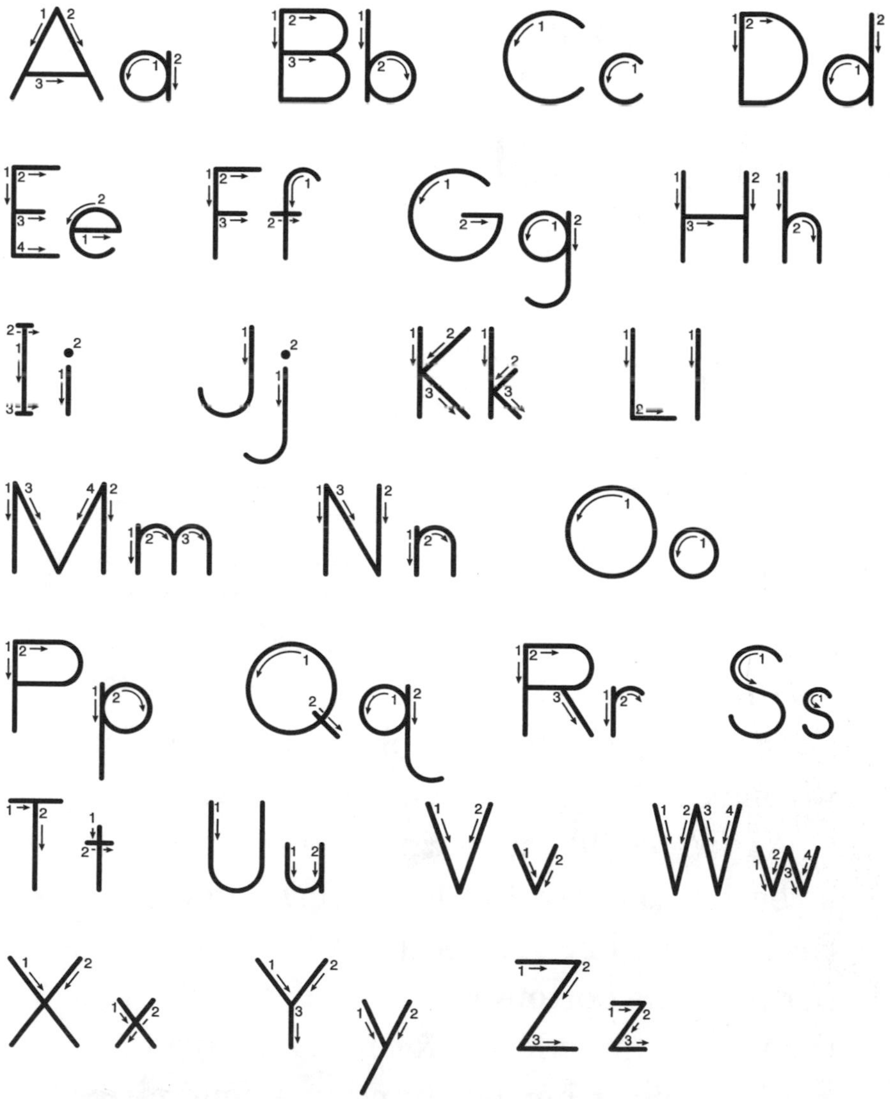

Aa Bb Cc Dd
Ee Ff Gg Hh
Ii Jj Kk Ll
Mm Nn Oo
Pp Qq Rr Ss
Tt Uu Vv Ww
Xx Yy Zz

Use the chart above to help you copy the
sentence at the top of the next page. Leave
a space as wide as your finger between
each word.

likes

YOUR NAME

to write.

To the parent: Have your child use a thick pencil. Grippers that are placed over regular pencils can be very helpful to new writers.

As your child copies the sentence, pay close attention to his or her letter formation. All circles should be formed from the top down—not from the bottom up. To cue your child to the proper circle letter formation, have him or her hold his or her left hand in a semi-circle. The forefinger is the correct starting place; the pencil moves counter-clockwise.

Skill: Letter Formation